JOURNEY OF MARCO POLO

MARCO POLO

Adapted by Dr. Marion Kimberly

GALLERY BOOKS
An Imprint of W. H. Smith Publishers Inc.
112 Madison Avenue
New York City 10016

© 1990 Ediciones B, S.A., Barcelona, Spain

This edition published 1991 by Gallery Books,
an imprint of W.H.Smith Publishers, Inc.,
112 Madison Avenue, New York, New York 10016

ISBN 0-8317-1462-X

Gallery Books are available for bulk purchase for sales
promotions and premium use. For details write or telephone
the Manager of Special Sales, W.H.Smith Publishers, Inc.,
112 Madison Avenue, New York, New York 10016. (212) 532-6600

Produced by Hawk Books Limited, London

Printed in Spain

Venice, 1296. The Genoans, encouraged by their recent victory over the Pisans, attack the beautiful city of Venice.

A few days after the famous battle of Curzola ...

Forward! Venice is ours!

The prisons of Genoa soon fill with captives ...

Amongst them a noble Patrician, captain of his own galley, Marco Polo...

You are in this cell with Rusticiano, a noble of Pisa ...

Is it true you're the Venetian Marco Polo? Famous for your travels?

Indeed, Sir.

At Rusticiano's request, Marco Polo passes the time by recounting some of his adventures, till one day ...

Why don't you write a book about all the marvels you have seen in far-off lands?

Oh no! I'm afraid I'm no scholar ...

Well my good friend, supposing I do the writing and you dictate - okay?

Well, if it will please you!

1

②

From Acre, we go on through Armenia and Baghdad ...

As you say brother.

In the following weeks they covered the first stages by sea in their own ship. Following the course of the Tigris, the travellers arrived at Hormuz in the Persian Gulf ...

We leave our ship here and go on to the land of the Great Khan by joining a sailing ship returning from the Indies.

But they found no ship that could take them ...

At the next city we'll buy horses.

I hate walking, brother!

Great! I love riding!

So it came to pass and the journey continued ...

Leaving behind the city of Karaman they passed through the mountains of Korassan.

Those mountains are known as the roof of the world.

This is the most difficult part of the journey ...

Never mind! Come on!

I envy your youthful enthusiasm, my son!

3

The weeks and months went by ... they crossed the Pamir plateau, forded rivers and survived deserts, eventually arriving in the land of China.

Look, the City of Tangut. We shall soon be at the Court of the Great Khan!

This is the Hwang-Ho river, meaning the yellow river, so called because it flows through sand which turns it bright yellow.

We are nearing Xanadu, the city of 108 temples, where the Great Khan will be residing now, as it is summer.

Marco's father was right, for a few hours later ...

You are lucky to speak the difficult Chinese language father!

I hope you'll soon learn the language, Marco.

And they rode into the fantastic city ...

Xanadu is half Mongolian, half Chinese.

It's ... it's marvellous!

... and arrived at the Imperial Palace ...

We have reached our goal my son ...

The Emperor expects you ... please enter ...

4

Marco - you are about to meet one of the most powerful men in the world!

I can't believe I'm to meet a descendant of the famous Genghis Khan!

One by one, the doors are opened ...

Powerful and Great Kubla Khan, the Emissaries of the Christian Pope are here ...

Welcome once again to my country, noble friends ...

This is my son, Marco, Great Khan!

I am pleased to meet you. Make yourselves at home.

Some hours later ...

Goodness! I don't recognize myself!

Having accepted these rich clothes you must learn the language ...

Having delivered the Pope's message and rich gifts to the Great Khan ...

I would like your son to meet my eldest son - come, Genghis!

I hope you'll become friends ...

Of course! How do you do, Genghis?

I trust my son will soon learn your beautiful language, Sir...

In my son's company he most certainly will ...!

Two months go by, then one day ...

It is true, my Lord, unless you conquer the City of Siaian-Fu you will not be Emperor of this part of China.

I know! I know! My faithful counsellor. But how can I conquer it? I've had it surrounded for three years!

What would it cost to conquer this city Great Khan? May I suggest...

Of course, Polo, my noble friend! Please speak.

Perhaps we can help you, Sir. If we were to build some war machines, the city might fall.

War machines? Of course you may. Go ahead!

The strange work went on for several days ...

But father, these are nothing more than simple catapults!

Simple catapults indeed Marco ...

... but here such weapons are entirely unknown! Look they're finished.

6

The great weapons amaze all who see them, including Kubla Khan ...

And you really hope to conquer the city with these my friend?

Hope and believe it, my Lord.

If you succeed I shall heap riches and honours upon you. Take the war machines to the battlefield!

Marco's father and uncle begged permission to go with the catapults. Two days later ...

God protect you, father!

Right, brother - forward!

Let's hope these catapults do the trick!

It took some days for the Polo brothers to reach the besieged city ...

There is our goal, Sir!

The Great Khan's soldiers, who'd been surrounding the city for three years, were puzzled by the war machines ...

You ... you think that can conquer the city?

Unbeliev-able!

It is amazing.

Ask them to collect rocks of around 300 lbs in weight ...

¡BROOUM!

There's complete panic in the city ...

Save your- selves!

Help!

The inhabitants, wholly overcome by the new weapons, lost no time in surrendering ...

Well done, foreigners!

You've won!

We never thought to gain such as easy victory!

Meanwhile the Court of the Great Khan has moved to Peking, the Imperial Capital ...

If you only knew how I long for news from Siaian-Fu, Marco!

Me too, my Lord.

But be assured my father and uncle will conquer the city for you ...

I believe so too, father!

And a few days later, came a messenger ...

You were right, Marco! The war machines have given us Siaian-Fu!

9

Return. Tell my generals that all honours shall be awarded to their men and them.

Your father and uncle be blessed a thousand times, Marco! They have given me a great victory!

The governors of the various states, hearing of the messengers' good news, sent presents to the Court to celebrate the Khan's triumph ...

Look father, here comes the first of the offerings.

Look, Lord, 100 white horses, a gift from the Governor of Kwang-Hai.

The Court and all the country was hung with white decorations ...

White is our symbol of happiness, Marco - don't be surprised if you see it everywhere ...

And many sumptuous feasts were held ...

10

But the greatest celebrations were left for the day of the conquering army's return ...

Father! Hurray!

Proudly bearing standards of dragons, moons, and stars ...

Long live the conquerors of Siaian-Fu!

Honour to the heroes!

Look father, the great war machines!

And after the great march past ...

I owe the most difficult victory of my life to you my friends ...I want you to stay with us forever!

Marco, his father and uncle remained in the Khan's service and were treated with great honour ...

From now on you will enjoy everything that goes with the high rank bestowed on you - as well as its responsibilities ...

Of course, Sir.

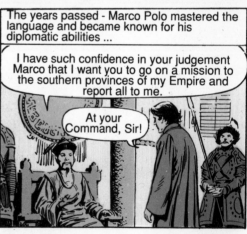

The years passed - Marco Polo mastered the language and became known for his diplomatic abilities ...

I have such confidence in your judgement Marco that I want you to go on a mission to the southern provinces of my Empire and report all to me.

At your Command, Sir!

Take this gold tablet with my seal and name and this safe conduct pass. Good luck, Marco!

Thank you Great Kubla Khan.

The next day ...

Go with God, my son

Marco Polo set off and having visited various beautiful cities in the Tiber region arrived in a certain area ...

Eh?

We are in Karadjan Sir! Look!

¡MUUUUUUu...!

The gigantic snakes here make it dangerous territory, Sir!

So I see, my friend.

Many days later the travellers find themselves in Karkan where the men ...

They seem to live like princes, here ...

But the women do all the work, Sir ...

How unjust! I'll tell the Great Khan he must change such customs.

Travelling onward to new territories, which even the Great Khan had never visited, Marco Polo reached ...

the Valley of the Great Rivers which flow from Tibet Sir! The Mekong River starts here.

Here begin the great jungles, full of elephants and rhinoceroses, Sir, and ignorant people who cover themselves in gold bracelets with no idea of their value ... we are in the Western region ...

Soon ...

Good Heavens!

Take care, Sir!

¡AUUULRG...!

We were lucky that time!

Marco's journey through China took six long months and on his return ...

My dear Marco you have carried out your diplomatic mission with great prudence as I knew you would. I am proud of you, my boy!

I intend to reward you with the Governorship of Yang-Chow province.

Thank you ... thank you ... Sir!

This is going too far! After all he is a foreigner!

I agree but if it's the Great Khan's wish ...

Marco Polo left for Yang-Chow to take up his post and in the city ...

In the name of the Great Kubla Khan, I intend to improve the customs of this province. Men and women will work equally together.

It is my wish that no one shall forget we are all human beings and I shall not tolerate injustice.

13

Meanwhile back in Peking ...

It is time that the island of Tsi-Pao became part of my Empire. I intend to attack it straight away!

You realize Tsi Pao belongs to Japan, brother?

You, Abatan and you, Bon-San-Chin, are two of my best generals. How do you feel about attacking Tsi-Pao?

But the two generals were old rivals in the art of strategy and came up with two very different plans ...

Your plan does not appeal to me Bon-San-Chin - I prefer Abatan's ...

I don't understand, Great Khan, ... mine is much better!

Enough! Leave me! Tomorrow the army leaves to invade Tsi-Pao.

I'll pay you back for this, Abatan ...

The Imperial fleet anchor outside the Japanese island ...

And a few days later Abatan ordered the men to disembark.

Look Bon-San-Chin, Abatan has ordered his men to disembark!

Without consulting me! With the deliberate intention of insulting me in front of my men.

(14)

But it's alright really, I shall seize command of his ships and leave him and his men ashore at the mercy of the enemy. I'll tell the Emperor they all perished ...

And so he did ... leaving them ...

Abatan! The Japanese!

What on earth is Bon-San-Chin doing? Where is he?

They soon succumbed to the enemy ...

Ah!

Fall back! Back to the ships!

But when they reached the shore ...

A thousand curses on Bon-San-Chin, the traitor! He's taken our ships!

Surrender! Surrender! If you don't want to die!

And so Abatan and his men were taken prisoners by the Japanese. Bon-San-Chin returned to Peking where ...

And you tell me Abatan and his 30,000 warriors were killed in Tsi-Pao - oh no!

I am sorry Great Kubla Khan ... we could not avoid defeat ...

Did you hear my friends? The Great Kubla Khan has had to hang up his sword to the Japanese. Marco, I'm so glad you are here to console me!

Some weeks later a message arrived at the Palace. The Japanese had disposed of their prisoners ...

This means that Bon-San-Chin is a miserable traitor!

Throw him into the dungeons - in days he shall be executed in public!

The sentence was carried out. Meanwhile, not far from Peking, in a city governed by Nayan the Great Khan's uncle ...

This is the best time to move against my nephew the Great Khan.

It is indeed. His armies are weakened after the attack on Tsi-Pao.

We shall join up with my friend Kaidu, and form an army capable of ending Kubla Khan's despotism.

Nayan's motives were entirely selfish and when the Great Khan heard the news ...

Miserable traitors! Don't they know I am the Great Khan!

Our armies will meet them on the plains before they get here!

Count on me Sir! Let me join the battle!

Some hours later.

Onward!

16

And the rebel army with Nayan at its head, set off too backed up by ...

FORWARD!

... ambitious Kaidu, also from court, who attacks the rearguard of Kubla Khan's army ...

Look out Great Khan! Over there!

And so the great battle raged ...

Consult the stars ... we want to know the Emperor's fate ...

What do you expect? Favourable or unfavourable signs for him in the battle?

What do you see? Tell me, I beg of you!

The Great Kubla Khan has fixed ideas about military strategy but he also has an adviser who does not believe in doing things by the book ...

You mean Marco Polo?

I do. The Emperor is fortunate in having such a sage adviser ...

Have you heard my friends? The battle signs are favourable!

We don't believe in omens but more in the strength of justice. And the Khan's cause is just.

Meanwhile, far away, the battle continues ...

Look out! On the flanks! We must guard our flanks!

Attack the flanks!

Marco Polo's tactics work ...

Look out! Here comes Nayan!

And in a few hours it turns into the greatest battle of ancient times -won by the Great Khan.

Death to the traitors!!

Long live the Emperor!

Victory!

18

You shan't get away, Nayan!

Defend yourself, foreigner!

Hold on, Nayan! I'll deal with him!

And just as Kaidu tried to stab him in the back ...

AAAH!

AH!

You will pay with your head for what you've done!

And so the conspiracy was crushed.

To Marco Polo ... the man who for so long has served me faithfully and brilliantly! And to his father and uncle!

19

So go friend, to your king and assure him I will send a beautiful bride.

A few days later a suitable princess is chosen as future Queen of Persia, a relative of the Khan.

And then came the moment of parting ...

I wish you every happiness in the future my friends. I shall never forget you.

Nor us, you Sir.

Goodbye Marco!

Goodbye - you've been like a brother to me.

And so

You're sure they have sufficient guards, Genghis?

They are carrying so many things of value ...

The best possible guard, father. We will ride to the port where the Emperor's ships await us.

God bless our long journey, son!

21

They arrived safely at the port and sailed to the island of Java and then on to Ceylon ...

Coming eventually to the city of Mailapun where they took a few days' rest ...

I see why they call this the Royal City of Peacocks!

It's amazing! They're everywhere.

And then to the City of Lar ...

Look father, Brahmins!

Yes, indeed, Marco. They spend their lives consulting the oracles - a strange Indian sect.

How much further do we have to go to reach the capital of Persia, Marco?

A long way still, dear Uncle - it will take about two months.

Changing ships they continued on their arduous journey ...

And two months later ...

Look, we've reached Hormuz!

Are you happy that you shall soon meet your future husband, King Argon?

Indeed I am, noble friend. And very grateful for all your care of me on this long journey.

The King of Persia prepared a great feast in their honour

22

It is our wish that you take part in the wedding festivities and join us in our happiness!

The festivities went on for days, at the end of which...

May the Gods bless you!

Well father we shall soon be in our beloved Venice.

So far we've nothing to complain of my son. A long but peaceful journey.

Having crossed Armenia and arrived at Trebisond, a Black Sea port, they finally embarked in a galley.

Greetings to the Great Khan, my friends!

And now for Venice! It seemed almost impossible at times ... twenty-five years we have been away from home.

23

24

Don't worry - we'll deal with them!

They're going to attack!

And when the Arab ship manoeuvres up to board them ...

We are ready for anything ... let's take them!

Give me a sword, I beg!

Here, Sir!

Soon the battle starts.

GET THEM!

Not so fast, friend!

Attack, lads! Attack!

But soon the pirates are forced to give up ...

Come! Set sail!

25

The tale of their adventures soon went all round Venice ...

And they say the Great Khan's Imperial treasure is increased by a hundred million ounces of silver every six months ...

And they say that the Great Khan's head-dress is worth ten million ...

Pietro, where are you going?

To the Polo's house; the house of millions!

And from then on their house was known as the house of millions.

But this is all worth millions, Marco.

It is only part of what we brought back my friends: costly carpets, tapestries, precious jewels and works of art ...

The stories you have to tell are wonderful Marco. Why don't you write a book?

Because I'm no scholar my friend.

And so the time passed until one day the Genoese attacked and Marco Polo was made prisoner ...

Such marvelous tales, Marco Polo, wonderful...

Aren't you tired with having written so much, Rusticiano?

I am not at all tired - do you know what...?

... it is not enough that you've told me all these stories ...

27

What else?

The whole world should read of your great travels to the Court of Kubla Khan!

Do you really think the tale of my adventures would interest the whole world?

Of course Marco! Your work must be published.

What you don't understand is that it could also be the means of giving us liberty Marco! I know Genoa wants to begin trading with other countries using Venice as a base.

I still don't understand, Rusticiano ...

Genoa could start trading with such far off countries as those you have visited and know so well ...

Without telling Marco, Rusticiano sent the manuscript to the Consul General of Genoa ...

From Rusticiano, Sir.

You waste my time with the Venetian captives' needs?

I know Sir, but Rusticiano insists it is in your interest to read this ...

What is all this? It seems to refer to Marco Polo, the other captive ...

28

It is amazing ... indeed ...

Consul Allieri was fascinated by the manuscript of Marco Polo's journeys.

I had no idea the captive, Marco Polo, had travelled so far - amazing!

And as Rusticiano had thought ...

I believe I know where Genoa might start trading ...

I don't understand, Sir!

I tell you there's a whole world of fabulous riches far beyond the Persian Gulf, my friend!

Quickly, go and release Marco Polo, I want to speak to him.

But when Marco realized what Rusticiano had done ...

How could you do this without telling me? It is my manuscript ...

Of course Marco! It's still yours ...

You are free Marco Polo. Consul Allieri awaits you!

Eh...?

I will not leave without my noble companion!

Allieri had to give in to Marco's demand and the two men found themselves in front of him.

I have read your story, Polo my friend. A man who has behaved with such goodness and wisdom cannot remain a captive of Genoa.

29

Listen carefully my friend. Genoa could trade with all these wealthy countries you have visited. I'd like you to lead the first trade mission with me!

Return to the Orient?

Perhaps, but I need rest now Consul Allieri. I want to stay in Venice and settle down for a while.

You are right friend. I hope one day you'll change your mind.

Thanks for what you did Rusticiano - God bless you!

I knew you'd thank me Marco! Goodbye my friend.

Marco returned to Venice where he was triumphantly received ...

Venice needs you my friend!

Will you stay here for good, Marco?

I can't tell you what I'll do - I just know I need a long rest ...

After many years of adventure, war, long journeys and finally captivity ... you'll understand.

He was made member of the Grand Council, Republic of Venice ...

... in which he remained, until he died in 1324.

His travels were over ... and Europe and the world lost one of its greatest men.

THE END

30